Made in the USA
Coppell, TX
19 February 2023

13087026R00063